KJARTAN POSKITT

WARP MAZE

To Alice +
Daniel –
Kjartan
Poskitt
19/10/02

DRAWN BY MR STEVEN APPLEBY
COLOUR BY NICOLA SHERRING

SCHOLASTIC
PRESS

Welcome to the strangest maze in the world

The Warp Maze is made up of different sections which are all linked together by Warp Doors. When you reach a Warp Door you can pass through it to any other door in the book that matches it. As you find your way round the book, you must try to collect all eight of these objects:

So where do you start?
The answer is here.

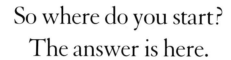

This is the ENTRANCE DOOR.

Look through the book to find the door that's exactly the same and then continue through the maze from there.

A bit of help to start you off: this door matches the door in the jewel box on the dressing table. You should be able to find a path through the pattern that leads you to the robot. (There, you've reached your first object already.) Now you can make your way back to the door in the jar, then you need to look through the book to see where that takes you. By the way, you'll see that you haven't been able to get to the urn. To reach it you'll have to wait until you find the Warp Door that takes you into the mirror.

Important: when you have all eight objects, you MUST find your way back to the Entrance door or you will be stuck for ever in the WARP!

Sometimes there might only be one other Warp Door you can go to, but at other times a Warp Door might have two or three matching doors. If you try one door and it doesn't get you very far, then find your way back and try another. You can double back and try again at any time.

HINT: Don't waste time trying to collect more than one of each object. There are a few spares in the maze which are impossible to reach.

The Sneex

Some sections of the Warp Maze have special rules. To make sure you don't cheat, you are being watched by the Sneex. There are at least 20 Sneex hiding around the Warp Maze. Can you spot the shapes of their eyes lurking in the shadows?

Warp Rating

You can check your Warp Rating by how many objects you've collected:

* four or less   Go back and try again!
* five   Warp Apprentice
* six   Warp Professional
* seven   Warp Expert
* eight   Warp Champion

HOT WATER OUT

COLD WATER IN

MAIN SEWAGE PIPE — ENTRY STRICTLY FORBIDDEN

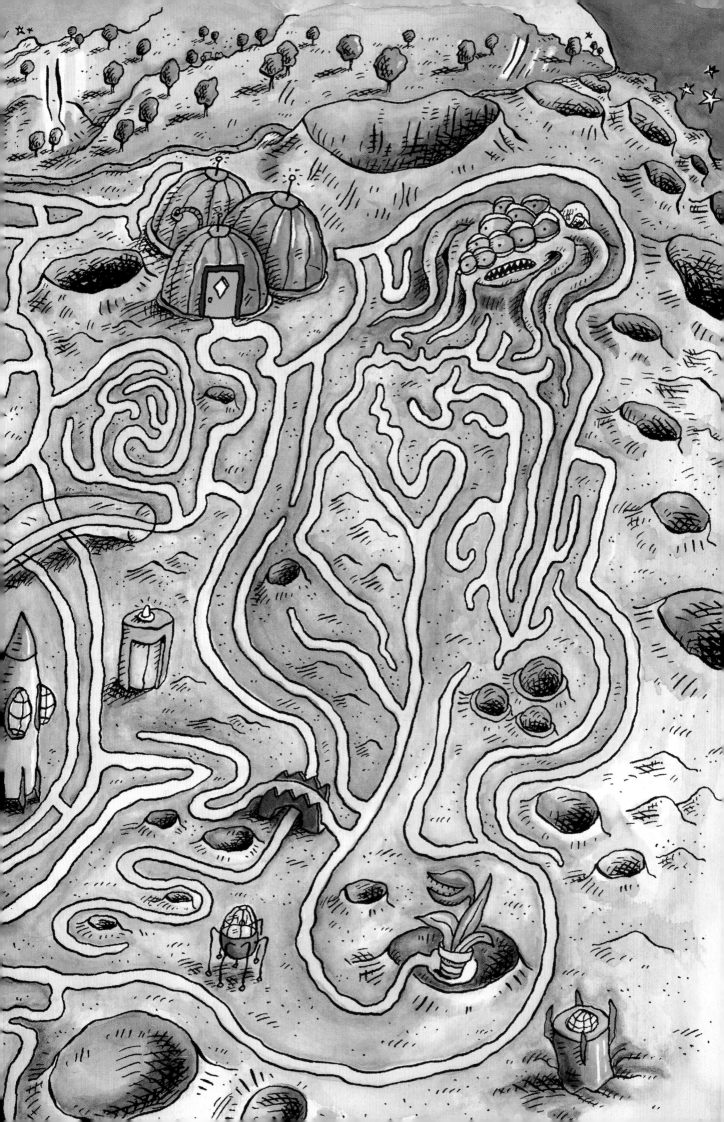

KEEP ON THE GRASS! DO NOT STEP OVER HOSEPIPES!

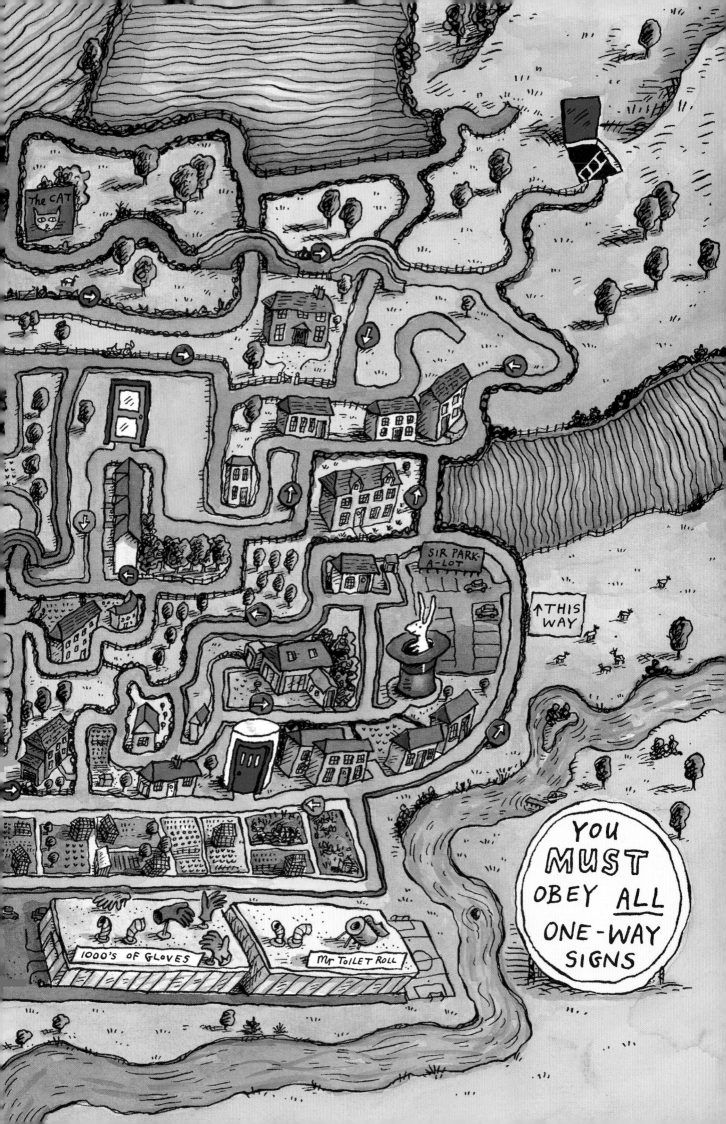

DO NOT
REVERSE
BY ORDER

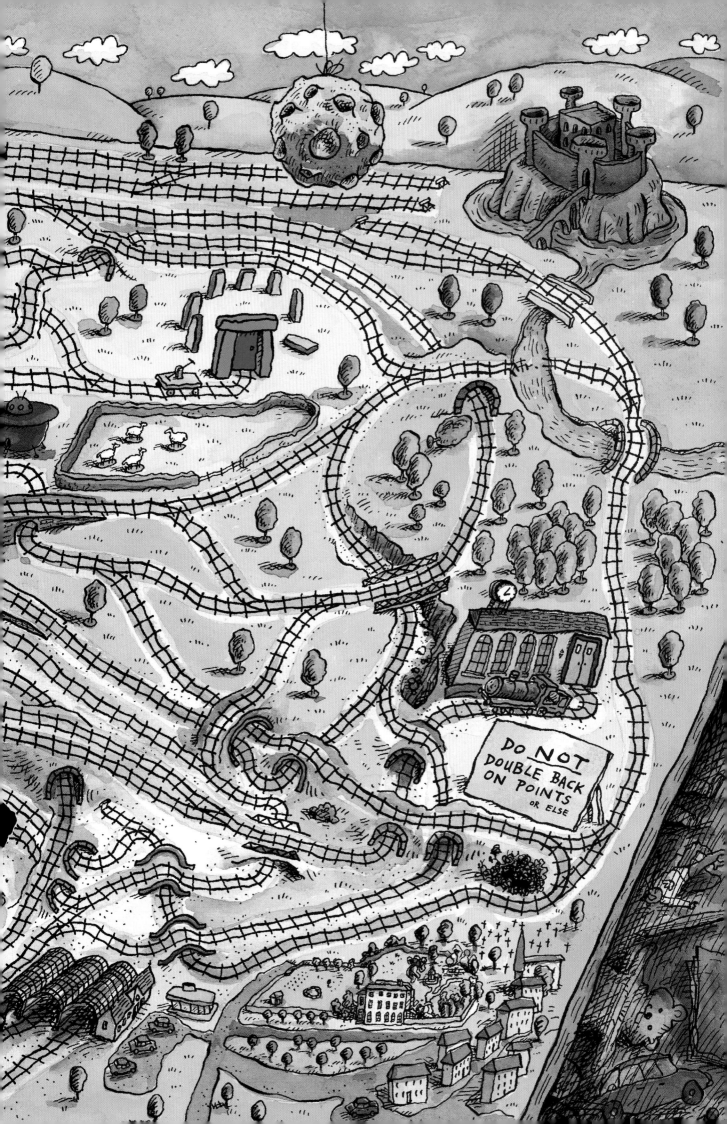

DO **NOT** DOUBLE BACK ON POINTS OR ELSE

For Maisie, Florence, Dulcie and Miranda
– K. P.

And for Tom, Alfie, Jasper and Clemmie
– S. A.

For hints and solutions go to www.warpmaze.com

Scholastic Children's Books,
Commonwealth House, 1-19 New Oxford Street,
London WC1A 1NU, UK

A division of Scholastic Ltd
London ~ New York ~ Toronto ~ Sydney ~ Auckland
Mexico City ~ New Delhi ~ Hong Kong

Published in the UK by Scholastic Ltd, 2002

Text copyright © Kjartan Poskitt, 2002
Illustrations copyright © Steven Appleby and Nicola Sherring, 2002

ISBN 0 439 99831 X

Printed by Oriental Press, Dubai, UAE

2 4 6 8 10 9 7 5 3 1

The right of Kjartan Poskitt, Steven Appleby and Nicola Sherring to be identified as author and illustrators of this work
respectively has been asserted by them in accordance with the Copyright, Designs and Patents Act, 1988.

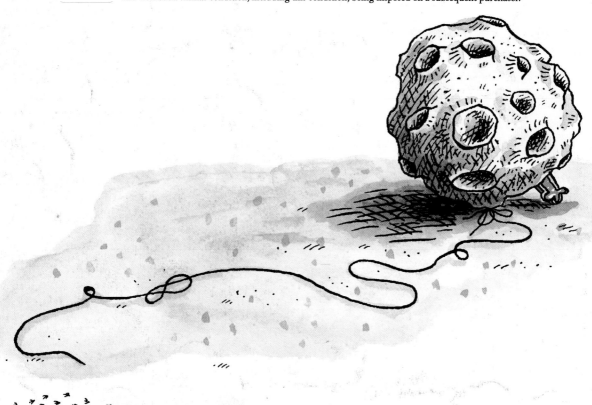